MW00608088

THE ULTIMATE
BOSTON CELTICS
TRIVIA BOOK

A Collection of Amazing Trivia Quizzes
and Fun Facts for Die-Hard Celtics Fans!

Ray Walker

978-1-953563-48-4

Copyright © 2021 by HRP House

ALL RIGHTS RESERVED

No part of this book may be reproduced, stored in a retrieval
system, or transmitted in any form or by any means, electronic,
mechanical, photocopying, recording, scanning, or otherwise,
without the prior written permission of the publisher.

Exclusive Free Book

Crazy Sports Stories

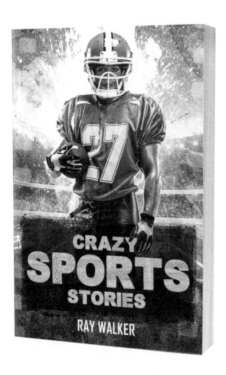

As a thank you for getting a copy of this book I would like to offer you a free copy of my book Crazy Sports Stories which comes packed with interesting stories from your favorite sports such as Football, Hockey, Baseball, Basketball and more.

Grab your free copy over at
RayWalkerMedia.com/Bonus

CONTENTS

INTRODUCTION

Team fandom should be inspirational. Our attachment to our favorite teams should fill us with pride, excitement, loyalty, and a sense of fulfillment in knowing that we are part of a community with many other fans who feel the same way.

Boston Celtics fans are no exception. With a rich, successful history in the NBA, the Celtics have inspired their supporters to strive for greatness with their tradition of colorful players, memorable eras, big moves, and unique moments.

This book is a celebration of those moments and an examination of the collection of interesting, impressive, and important details that allow us to understand the full stories behind the players and the team.

You may use the book as you wish. Each chapter contains 20 quiz questions in a mixture of multiple-choice and true-false formats, an answer key (don't worry, it's on a separate page!), and a section of 10 "Did You Know" facts about the team.

Some will use it to test themselves with the quiz questions. How much Celtics history did you really know? How many of the finer points can you remember? Some will use it competitively (isn't that the heart of sports?), waging contests with friends and fellow devotees to see who can lay claim to being the biggest fan. Some will enjoy it as a learning experience, gaining insight to enrich their fandom and add color to their understanding of their favorite team. Still others may use it to teach, sharing the wonderful anecdotes inside to inspire a new generation of fans to hop aboard the Boston bandwagon.

Whatever your purpose may be, we hope you enjoy delving into the amazing background of Boston Celtics basketball!

Oh… for the record, information and statistics in this book are current up to the beginning of 2021. The Celtics will surely topple more records and win more awards as the seasons pass, so keep this in mind when you're watching the next game with your friends and someone starts a conversation with "Did you know…?"

CHAPTER 1:

ORIGINS & HISTORY

QUIZ TIME!

1. In which year did the Boston Celtics begin playing in the National Basketball Association?

    a. 1946
    b. 1949
    c. 1952
    d. 1956

2. The franchise was nearly called the Boston Brewers, partly to reflect the significance of the alcohol industry in the New England market and partly to honor a defunct baseball team from the city by that name.

    a. True
    b. False

3. How was the nickname "Celtics" chosen for the team?

    a. The team's first owner also owned Celtic F.C., a soccer club in the Scottish Premiership, and wanted his sports franchises to align.

b. The name suggested mysticism and historical significance, factors that the founders believed would make the team appear established and help sell tickets.

c. It was selected to match the name of a brand of tea that was very popular in Boston after World War II.

d. It reflected the Irish heritage of many Boston residents and honored the nickname of a previous basketball team from New York.

4. In which season did the Celtics begin to play in their new arena (TD Garden)?

   a. 1991-92
   b. 1995-96
   c. 1999-2000
   d. 2005-06

5. Who was the founder of the Boston Celtics?

   a. Charles Adams
   b. Robert G. Schmertz
   c. Red Auerbach
   d. Walter A. Brown

6. In which season did the Celtics earn their first playoff berth?

   a. 1946-47
   b. 1947-48
   c. 1950-51
   d. 1953-54

7. No other city has hosted more NBA All-Star Games than Boston, which hosted the first two ever played and has hosted a total of four.

   a. True
   b. False

8. How many division titles have the Celtics won?

   a. 17
   b. 19
   c. 25
   d. 31

9. Who was the first Celtic ever to be named as Boston's representative in the NBA All-Star Game?

   a. Center Bill Russell
   b. Guard John Havlicek
   c. Forward Ed Macauley
   d. Forward Larry Bird

10. Where do the Boston Celtics rank among NBA franchises in Larry O'Brien Championship Trophies won?

    a. 1st overall, with 16 titles
    b. Tied for 2nd overall with the Chicago Bulls, with 14 titles
    c. 5th overall, with 9 titles
    d. Tied for 1st overall with the Los Angeles Lakers, with 17 titles each

11. How did the Celtics fare during their first season at TD Garden after leaving their memorable former home, the Boston Garden?

a. Finished 8th in the conference and lost in the first round

b. Finished 11th in the conference and missed the playoffs

c. Finished 1st in the conference and won the NBA championship

d. Finished 4th in the conference and lost in the semifinals

12. The Celtics' longest stretch of missing the playoffs was six years in a row from 1995 to 2001. Aside from that, they have never failed to qualify for the playoffs for more than two years in a row.

a. True

b. False

13. Which team did Boston face in its first-ever NBA game (which resulted in a 59-53 loss)?

a. Chicago Stags

b. Detroit Falcons

c. Providence Steamrollers

d. St. Louis Bombers

14. Boston's current top development team plays in the NBA G League. What is this team called?

a. Connecticut Celtics

b. Massachusetts Mean Machine

c. New England Irishmen

d. Maine Red Claws

15. Which player poured in a whopping 9 points and finished as the top scorer in the first-ever NBA game that the Boston Celtics played?

  a. Red Wallace
  b. Connie Simmons
  c. Art Spector
  d. Wyndol Gray

16. As of 2020, Boston is tied with the Los Angeles Lakers and Detroit Pistons as the NBA franchise that has sent the most players to the Summer Olympics to represent their countries.

  a. True
  b. False

17. How did Boston fare in its first-ever NBA playoff run?

  a. Lost in the first round to the Chicago Stags
  b. Lost in the division semifinals to the New York Knicks
  c. Lost in the division finals to the Syracuse Nationals
  d. Won the NBA championship by defeating the Atlanta Hawks

18. The Celtics have accumulated more regular seasons with at least 60 victories than any other NBA franchise. How many times have they met or exceeded this mark?

  a. 13
  b. 16
  c. 20
  d. 22

19. What is the name of the Celtics' team mascot?

    a. Charlie Celtic
    b. Irish Ira
    c. Lucky the Leprechaun
    d. Johnny O'Beantown

20. In 2005, while looking for a permanent sponsor, the Boston Celtics auctioned off naming rights for their home arena once a day and cycled through 30 different names; although, the team rejected one winning bidder who wanted to call the arena the Derek Jeter Center.

    a. True
    b. False

QUIZ ANSWERS

1. A – 1946

2. B – False

3. D – It reflected the Irish heritage of many Boston residents and honored the nickname of a previous basketball team from New York.

4. B – 1995-96

5. D – Walter A. Brown

6. B – 1947-48

7. B – False

8. D – 31

9. C – Forward Ed Macauley

10. D – Tied for 1st overall with the Los Angeles Lakers, with 17 titles each

11. B – Finished 11th in the conference and missed the playoffs

12. A – True

13. C – Providence Steamrollers

14. D – Maine Red Claws

15. A – Red Wallace

16. B – False

17. A – Lost in the first round to the Chicago Stags

18. A – 13

19. C – Lucky the Leprechaun

20. A – True

DID YOU KNOW?

1. As an original member team of the NBA, Boston has fittingly not been shuffled around much during conference or division realignment. In fact, they have changed only once. The team has always played in the NBA's East Conference. From 1946 to 1969, they were in the Eastern Division and, since 1970, they have been slotted into the Atlantic Division.

2. Boston had been home to two professional basketball teams before the Celtics arrived, but neither had nearly the success that the Celtics went on to. Both the Boston Whirlwinds and the Boston Trojans played in the American Basketball League, and each lasted just one season, 1925 and 1934, respectively.

3. The Celtics were one of 11 original teams from 1946 to play in the league that would become the National Basketball Association. Only three of those original franchises remain in the league today, and since the Philadelphia Warriors moved to Golden State, only the Celtics and New York Knicks retain both their original city and nickname.

4. While the Celtics are an anchor tenant of the TD Garden, it is not their home exclusively. The arena configuration shrinks, losing about 1,050 seats, to house the National Hockey League's Boston Bruins, and expands by about 1,400 seats when musical acts or other entertainment

comes to town. The Boston Blazers lacrosse team previously played in the Garden as well.

5. As a new team entering the NBA in 1946, the Celtics paid a $1,000 franchise fee for the right to join the league. Their original salary cap that year was $30,000. For context, when the Toronto Raptors joined in 1993, they paid an expansion fee of $125 million and the NBA salary cap is currently just over $109 million.

6. The first time a backboard was ever broken in the NBA occurred in Boston in 1946. Although the backboards were wooden at the time, an exuberant dunk in the pregame warm-ups caused both damage to the backboard and an hour-long delay before the game could begin.

7. Boston's biggest NBA rival is generally thought to be the Los Angeles Lakers because both teams have found multiple eras of sustained success and have faced off against each other in the NBA Finals twelve times. The Celtics have the advantage in the head-to-head rivalry, with a record of 161-131, leaving the Lakers with just a .449 winning percentage against them.

8. The Celtics have a knack for celebrating their anniversary seasons in style. The franchise won NBA titles during its 20th, 30th, and 40th seasons in the league.

9. Other nicknames strongly considered for Boston's basketball team at its creation include the Whirlwinds, the Unicorns, and the Olympians.

10. In the beginning, it took a little time for the Boston Celtics to find their footing in the league. They began play in 1946 and finished with a losing record in their first four seasons. Over the next 27 years, they established a much more successful tradition of excellence and only one of those seasons ended with a sub-.500 record.

CHAPTER 2:

JERSEYS & NUMBERS

QUIZ TIME!

1. When they began playing in the NBA in 1946, the Celtics used what color scheme for their home and away uniforms?

    a. Green and gold
    b. Red, white, and blue
    c. Green and white
    d. Black, green, and orange

2. The numbers 0 and 00 have been banned from circulation by Boston's ownership because they are seen to represent a losing attitude.

    a. True
    b. False

3. The modern-day Celtics use which five colors in their official NBA logo?

    a. Green, white, yellow, blue, and gray
    b. Green, white, orange, black, and red

c. Green, white, gold, brown, and black

d. Green, gold, blue, silver, and white

4. Which famous Boston Celtic starred in an Adidas commercial that referenced his jersey number with the memorable tagline "That's me, employee No. 8. I make baskets"?

  a. Guard Ray Allen

  b. Forward Antoine Walker

  c. Guard Danny Ainge

  d. Forward Wally Szczerbiak

5. When Boston designed a special Christmas jersey in 2016, what did they change about their regular uniform?

  a. The colors: adding red to go with their green and white for Christmas

  b. The design: adding sleeves where there were usually none

  c. The font: using script writing instead of their usual block lettering

  d. The logo: displaying their leprechaun logo on the chest instead of words

6. Which jersey number has proven to be most popular with Boston, having been worn by 34 players?

  a. 4

  b. 11

  c. 12

  d. 20

7. The highest number ever retired by the Boston Celtics is No. 35, belonging to Reggie Lewis.

   a. True
   b. False

8. Before the year 2000, only one Celtic had ever worn a number above 55. Who was it?

   a. Forward Brandon Hunter, wearing 56
   b. Center Acie Earl, wearing 75
   c. Forward Roy Rogers, wearing 99
   d. Center Greg Stiemsma, wearing 83

9. Why did star forward Larry Bird choose to wear No. 33 on his jersey?

   a. He believed Kareem Abdul-Jabbar was the greatest player of all time and wanted to become the best himself.
   b. His brother Mark wore the number in high school and Larry looked up to his brother.
   c. He claimed that he wanted "as many 3's as possible because that's how I'm going to shoot."
   d. His original plan was to retire at age 33 and go back to French Lick to raise a family.

10. Forward P.J. Brown is the only Celtic ever to wear which of the following uniform numbers?

    a. 63
    b. 73
    c. 83
    d. 93

11. Which unusual color have the Celtics worn occasionally to celebrate something specific?

    a. Pink, to celebrate Valentine's Day

    b. Orange, to celebrate Halloween

    c. Gray, to celebrate historic franchise moments

    d. Red, to celebrate former coach and general manager Red Auerbach

12. Star point guard K.C. Jones is the only Celtic ever to have worn the No. 25 on his jersey and will continue to be the only one because his number is now retired.

    a. True

    b. False

13. When the Celtics acquired superstar Kevin Garnett, who had worn No. 21 for over a decade with the Minnesota Timberwolves, why did Garnett choose to wear No. 5 on the back of his jersey instead for Boston?

    a. He wanted to signify a fresh start with his new team.

    b. The No. 5 represented the five players on the court, showing that Garnett valued teamwork and was not arriving to put up superstar numbers himself.

    c. Number 21 had been retired in Boston, for guard Bill Sharman.

    d. Garnett had added weight and felt that 5 made him look slimmer than 21.

14. How many single-digit jersey numbers have the Boston Celtics retired?

a. 2

b. 4

c. 8

d. 10

15. Which two players competed for the Celtics for just six seasons, the shortest tenure of anyone whose number has been retired by the franchise?

    a. Guard Dennis Johnson and forward Kevin McHale

    b. Forwards Cedric Maxwell and Jim Loscutoff

    c. Center Robert Parish and guard Sam Jones

    d. Center Ed Macauley and swingman Reggie Lewis

16. Twelve players have worn the No. 1 for Boston and every single one of them was a point guard.

    a. True

    b. False

17. Lucky No. 7 has been worn by 20 Celtic players over the years. Which athlete wore it for the longest amount of time?

    a. Point guard Art Williams

    b. Point guard Tiny Archibald

    c. Point guard Dee Brown

    d. Swingman Jaylen Brown

18. Who is the most recent Celtic player to have his number retired by the club?

    a. Shooting guard Ray Allen

    b. Small forward Cedric Maxwell

c. Power forward Antoine Walker

d. Small forward Paul Pierce

19. Which number did center Ed Macauley, who was named the first All-Star in Celtic history, wear on the back of his jersey in 1950-51?

a. 1

b. 11

c. 22

d. 33

20. During the 1980s, the Celtics agreed to participate in a game against the Detroit Pistons without wearing jerseys. The game was marketed as "Shirts vs. Skins" and was a major success as a publicity stunt.

a. True

b. False

QUIZ ANSWERS

1. C – Green and white

2. B – False

3. C – Green, white, gold, brown, and black

4. B – Forward Antoine Walker

5. C – The font: using script writing instead of their usual block lettering

6. C – 12

7. A – True

8. C – Forward Roy Rogers, wearing 99

9. B – His brother Mark wore the number in high school and Larry looked up to his brother.

10. D – 93

11. C – Gray, to celebrate historic franchise moments

12. A – True

13. C – No. 21 had been retired in Boston, for guard Bill Sharman.

14. B – 4

15. D – Center Ed Macauley and swingman Reggie Lewis

16. B – False

17. C – Point guard Dee Brown

18. D – Small forward Paul Pierce

19. C – 22

20. B – False

DID YOU KNOW?

1. The No. 1 was retired by the Boston Celtics, but not because a player ever wore it. Instead, the Celtics took the number out of circulation in honor of founder Walter A. Brown.

2. The Celtics already own the record for most retired numbers by any professional sports team in North America. Currently, 22 numbers hang from the rafters in TD Garden and the team has announced plans to make that 23 in the near future when Kevin Garnett's No. 5 joins the group.

3. Six players have worn the No. 0 for the Celtics, but only one has ever donned 00. Center Robert Parish put two zeroes on his back during his lengthy tenure in Boston. Parish had worn the number since his high school days, stating that it was the only jersey left when he began playing.

4. Boston felt the need to pay homage to the franchise's greatest architect, Red Auerbach, so they retired the No. 2 to represent him, despite Auerbach never playing a minute in that (or any) jersey number for the Celtics.

5. Celtics broadcaster Johnny Most, who was with the team from 1953 to 1990, has a banner hanging in Boston's rafters. Since he did not wear a number, Most's banner sports a picture of a microphone on it.

6. While it's certainly a rare honor for a player to have his number retired by the Boston Celtics, guard Jo Jo White can boast more than just his No. 10 in the rafters at TD Garden. White also had his No. 15 retired at the University of Kansas and made it into the Marine Corps Sports Hall of Fame.

7. Superstition may have scared some Celtics away from wearing the No. 13. Although 20 players in franchise history have chosen it for themselves, only Delonte West, who wore it from 2005 to 2011, has kept the number for more than a few years.

8. Only three Celtics have ever worn a jersey with a number higher than 55 for longer than a single season before switching numbers or leaving the team. Amir Johnson sported No. 90 for two seasons, and Jae Crowder and Tacko Fall have both worn No. 99 in multiple years.

9. Current Boston center Tacko Fall had a personal reason for choosing No. 99 for the Celtics. Fall selected the uncommon number because of his Muslim faith. It pays homage to the 99 Names of Allah.

10. Small forward Jim Loscutoff played well enough for the team that the Celtics offered to retire his No. 18. Loscutoff appreciated the honor but wanted the number to stay in circulation for other players, so Boston hung a banner with his nickname "Loscy" instead. The No. 18 was later retired to honor center Dave Cowens.

CHAPTER 3:

CATCHY NICKNAMES

QUIZ TIME!

1. By which franchise nickname are the Celtics most commonly referred to?

    a. "C-Green Smash Machine"

    b. "The Bean Towners"

    c. "The Celts"

    d. "The Birds"

2. Celtic guard Sam Jones was often referred to as "Sammy Davis" thanks to his exciting play and resemblance to entertainer Sammy Davis Jr.

    a. True

    b. False

3. The longtime home of the Celtics, Boston Garden, was also more commonly known by which popular nickname?

    a. "Madison Round"

    b. "The Factory"

    c. "Boston Common"

    d. "The Garden"

4. Which Celtic player was such a natural at the game of basketball that he received the nickname "Easy"?

    a. Forward Paul Pierce
    b. Forward Ed Macauley
    c. Guard Dee Brown
    d. Center Bill Russell

5. French center Vincent Poirier, standing seven feet tall, was known by which nickname during his time with the Celtics?

    a. "Le Grand Baguette"
    b. "The French Connection"
    c. "The French Irishman"
    d. "Sacre Bleu"

6. Which of the following is NOT a nickname that was given to Celtic forward Kevin Garnett?

    a. "The Kid"
    b. "The Big Ticket"
    c. "The Green Monster"
    d. "The Franchise"

7. Current Celtic forward Semi Ojeleye has perhaps the most impressive nickname of anyone in the league, let alone in Boston. Ojeleye is known as "Muscles Jesus."

    a. True
    b. False

8. Because of his nationality and size, Celtic center Vitaly Potapenko was often referred to by which of the following nicknames?

a. "The Russian Bear"

b. "The Ukraine Train"

c. "The Serbian Sumo"

d. "The Croatian Caveman"

9. Among all the players in Boston's storied NBA history, which one can claim to be the most representative of the franchise because he has earned the nickname "Mr. Celtic"?

a. Larry Bird

b. Bill Russell

c. Tom Heinsohn

d. Bob Cousy

10. For what reason did Celtics teammate Danny Ainge refer to power forward Kevin McHale as "The Black Hole of the Low Post"?

a. Because McHale consumed everyone in his path, letting nothing stop him from getting to the basket.

b. Because everything in the Celtics offense was designed to orbit around McHale once he got to that spot.

c. Because when Ainge passed the ball to McHale in that area, it would never come back out to other Celtics again.

d. Because McHale had such an array of moves that no one ever knew what would happen to an opposing player if he tried to get close to defend.

11. Which Celtic player was known to fans and teammates by the nickname "The Truth"?

a. Forward Paul Pierce

b. Center Eric Montross

c. Guard Kyrie Irving

d. Center Danny Fortson

12. After engaging in two memorable fights with his former New York Knicks teammates as a newly traded member of the Boston Celtics, forward Xavier McDaniel earned the nickname "The Vengeful X."

a. True

b. False

13. Why is current Celtic forward Jayson Tatum known to teammates by the nickname "Taco Jay"?

a. Because Tatum has a habit of scoring Boston's 100th point at home games, which earns every fan in attendance a free taco.

b. It is a play on words related to how Tatum pronounces teammate Tacko Fall's first name.

c. Because of Tatum's frequent celebratory hugs, in which he wraps his arms around teammates like the shell of a taco.

d. Because of Tatum's memorable Instagram posts of himself devouring heaps of tacos.

14. For what reason did Celtic center Shaquille O'Neal refer to himself in the media as "the Big Aristotle"?

a. He was excited about having gone back to Louisiana State University to earn his degree many years after having left early for the NBA draft.

b. He playfully spoke about learning a great deal of philosophy under Boston coach Doc Rivers' tutelage.

c. He wanted to be known for his intelligence as well as his obvious physicality.

d. He loved a quote from the philosopher Aristotle, who said that "excellence is not a singular act; it's a habit. You are what you repeatedly do."

15. Celtic forward Larry Bird was referred to by all of the following nicknames except for which one?

a. "Larry Legend"
b. "The Birdman of Boston"
c. "The Hick from French Lick"
d. "The Great White Hope"

16. Boston forward Kevin Garnett was called "Uncle KG" by his young teammates because he was brought in to provide leadership and playoff experience while demonstrating how to act as a professional athlete.

a. True
b. False

17. Iconic Celtic swingman John Havlicek was nicknamed "Hondo" after a movie starring which Hollywood icon?

a. Cary Grant
b. Humphrey Bogart
c. John Wayne
d. Clint Eastwood

18. Current Celtic television color commentator Brian Scalabrine is a former Boston power forward who went by which nickname during his time with the team?

    a. "Scales"
    b. "White Mamba"
    c. "Captain Briny"
    d. "Brine Brine"

19. Current Celtic radio color commentator Cedric Maxwell is a former Boston small forward who went by which nickname during his time with the team?

    a. "Cedric the Entertainer"
    b. "Mad Max"
    c. "C.M. Punk"
    d. "Cornbread"

20. Boston center Robert Parish was nicknamed "The Chief" because his facial features and lack of expression were similar to a character who went by that name in the Hollywood hit movie *One Flew Over the Cuckoo's Nest*.

    a. True
    b. False

QUIZ ANSWERS

1. C – "The Celts"

2. B – False

3. D – "The Garden"

4. B – Forward Ed Macauley

5. A – "Le Grand Baguette"

6. C – "The Green Monster"

7. A – True

8. B – "The Ukraine Train"

9. C – Tom Heinsohn

10. C – Because when Ainge passed the ball to McHale in that area, it would never come back out to other Celtics again.

11. A – Forward Paul Pierce

12. B – False

13. D – Because of Tatum's memorable Instagram posts of himself devouring heaps of tacos.

14. D – He loved a quote from the philosopher Aristotle, who said that "excellence is not a singular act; it's a habit. You are what you repeatedly do."

15. B – "The Birdman of Boston"

16. B – False

17. C – John Wayne

18. B – "White Mamba"

19. D – "Cornbread"

20. A – True

DID YOU KNOW?

1. Boston center Pervis Ellison had to take the good with the bad when it came to nicknames. Teammates dubbed him "Never Nervous Pervis" for his clutch performances in pressure-packed situations but, after a series of injuries prevented him from seeing much of the floor, he was also christened "Out of Service Pervis."

2. Celtics icon Larry Bird was given many nicknames throughout his career, but his first coach in Boston, Bill Fitch, settled on "Kodak." The moniker came out of Fitch's respect for Bird's ability to create a mental picture of where all 10 players were on the court, just like a camera.

3. The great Bill Russell was such an intimidating defensive presence for the Celtics that even his blocks had a nickname. Sportswriters referred to them as "Wilsonburgers" after the brand of the basketballs that Russell swatted back into opponents' faces.

4. For nearly a decade, from the late 1950s to the late 1960s, Boston's backcourt featured a duo known as "The Jones Boys." Point guard K.C. Jones and shooting guard Sam Jones led the team to a fantastic run of success that included eight championships.

5. Boston icon Bob Cousy was once shunned by the team in the NBA draft, with coach Red Auerbach dubbing him a "local yokel." Eventually, Cousy did end up with the

franchise and became more reverently known as "the Houdini of the Hardwood" because of his ball-handling and passing skills.

6. The Celtics' frontcourt in the 1980s was one of the most impressive of all time in the NBA. It featured three players who made the NBA's 50th Anniversary All-Time Team: center Robert Parish and forwards Larry Bird and Kevin McHale. Collectively, this trio was known as "The Big Three."

7. A second group of Celtics was also given the "Big Three" moniker in 2008, when longtime Boston forward Paul Pierce was joined by new acquisitions Kevin Garnett and Ray Allen to lead the team to another NBA championship.

8. Boston power forward Kevin McHale was such a difficult assignment for opposing players to guard that the task received its own nickname. Anyone charged with defending him in the low post area was said to be in McHale's "Torture Chamber."

9. Despite many sharpshooting aces in team history, guard Sam Jones is the Boston Celtic perhaps most remembered for his proficiency. Jones's skill and form, especially on bank shots, led to his nickname as "The Shooter."

10. The history of Celtic center Shaquille O'Neal's nicknames is a long one. He has cycled through "Shaq," "Superman," "Diesel," "M.D.E" (Most Dominant Ever), "L.C.L" (Last Center Left), "Wilt Chamberneazy," "Osama Bin Shaq," "The Big Aristotle," "The Big Deporter," "The Big Felon," and "The Big Sidekick."

CHAPTER 4:

ALMA MATERS

QUIZ TIME!

1. Hall of Fame guard Sam Jones was not as highly scouted as many other players because he attended which little-known college?

    a. Hawaii State University

    b. Loyola-Marymount University

    c. Midwestern State University

    d. North Carolina Central University

2. The Celtics have drafted more players from the Michigan State Spartans than from the Michigan Wolverines.

    a. True

    b. False

3. Guard Paul Westphal played four years of college ball for which program before being drafted by the Celtics?

    a. University of Southern California

    b. Southern Methodist University

c. Texas Southern University

d. Southern New Hampshire University

4. First-ever Celtics draft choice Bulbs Ehlers attended Purdue University, where he played for the basketball team that went by which nickname?

a. The Rainbows

b. The Boilermakers

c. The Fightin' Rebels

d. The Yellowjackets

5. Of the five players Boston has selected from the following college basketball programs, from which school did the Celtics draft the most successful NBA player?

a. Texas Longhorns

b. Texas A&M Aggies

c. Texas Tech Red Raiders

d. Texas-El Paso Miners

6. Legendary Celtic guard John Havlicek played his college ball at Ohio State University, where he was a teammate of which future legendary basketball coach?

a. Phil Jackson

b. Pat Riley

c. John Thompson

d. Bobby Knight

7. Fan favorite Tony Allen is the only player the Celtics have ever selected from Oklahoma State University.

a. True

b. False

8. Forward Tom Sanders played for New York University before starring with the Celtics. What was his college team's nickname?

   a. The Knickerbockers
   b. The Brokers
   c. The Violets
   d. The Founders

9. The Celtics selected two teammates from Syracuse University in the 2012 NBA draft. Which teammates did they choose with the 22nd overall and 51st overall picks?

   a. Jared Sullinger and Avery Bradley
   b. Fab Melo and Kris Joseph
   c. E'Twaun Moore and James Young
   d. J.R. Giddens and Jordan Mickey

10. Top overall pick Chuck Share played his college basketball as the center for which program before coming to the Celtics?

    a. Bowling Green University
    b. University of Maryland
    c. Duke University
    d. Georgetown University

11. Only three Ivy League players have played for the Celtics after being drafted by them. Which brainy school never produced an NBA player for Boston?

    a. Yale University
    b. University of Pennsylvania

c. Harvard University

d. Brown University

12. The Celtics have used the prep-to-pro method by drafting a player directly out of high school.

a. True

b. False

13. Forward Jared Sullinger was drafted by the Celtics out of which school that is better known as a football powerhouse than a basketball school?

a. University of Miami

b. Clemson University

c. University of Alabama

d. Ohio State University

14. The Celtics drafted two players from the Kansas Jayhawks who would go on to play more than 800 NBA games each. Who were these players?

a. Brian Shaw and Jeff Green

b. Jo Jo White and Paul Pierce

c. Cedric Maxwell and Tom Sanders

d. Danny Ainge and Joe Johnson

15. Which player, drafted by the Celtics from the Iowa Hawkeyes, went on to have the best NBA career?

a. Rick Williams

b. Acie Earl

c. Brad Lohaus

d. Steve Waite

16. Center John Richter, who was chosen 6ᵗʰ overall in 1959, is the highest-drafted player the Celtics have ever selected from North Carolina State University.

    a. True
    b. False

17. For which college program did Lithuanian center Darius Songaila play?

    a. University of Tennessee
    b. Providence University
    c. Georgia Tech University
    d. Wake Forest University

18. Two players were teammates in college with the Kansas Jayhawks before taking the court together in Boston as well. Which two players were they?

    a. Guard Dee Brown and forward Antoine Walker
    b. Center Vitaly Potapenko and guard Rajon Rondo
    c. Center Raef LaFrentz and forward Paul Pierce
    d. Forward Jayson Tatum and center Al Horford

19. The high-scoring Reggie Lewis was a member of which college squad before his time on the court with the Celtics?

    a. University of New Mexico
    b. Rice University
    c. Northeastern University
    d. Syracuse University

20. Due to their longstanding rivalry with the Los Angeles Lakers, Boston has never drafted a player from the UCLA Bruins.

    a. True

    b. False

QUIZ ANSWERS

1. D – North Carolina Central University

2. B – False

3. A – University of Southern California

4. B – The Boilermakers

5. A – Texas Longhorns

6. D – Bobby Knight

7. B – False

8. C – The Violets

9. B – Fab Melo and Kris Joseph

10. A – Bowling Green University

11. C – Harvard University

12. A – True

13. D – Ohio State University

14. B – Jo Jo White and Paul Pierce

15. C – Brad Lohaus

16. A – True

17. D – Wake Forest University

18. C – Center Raef LaFrentz and forward Paul Pierce

19. C – Northeastern University

20. B – False

DID YOU KNOW?

1. The Celtics have a penchant for drafting teammates from the University of Kentucky Wildcats. They selected three players from the school in 1953, two more in 1960, and then used back-to-back 6th overall picks in 1996 and 1997 on Wildcat duo Antoine Walker and Ron Mercer.

2. Boston has made two Oregon Ducks players top-10 picks in the NBA draft. The team selected forward Jim Loscutoff 3rd overall in 1955 and guard Jim Barnett 8th overall in 1966.

3. As a member of the Wichita State Shockers, future Celtic forward Xavier McDaniel had an incredible senior season. In 1984-85, McDaniel averaged 27.4 points, 15 rebounds per game, making him the first athlete ever to lead the nation in both categories during the same year.

4. Ronnie Williams is the only Florida Gator ever taken by the Boston Celtics in an NBA draft. Williams was selected in the 2nd round in 1984 but never made it into an NBA game.

5. Before being drafted by the Boston Celtics, center Eric Montross starred for the University of North Carolina Tar Heels. Montross helped them win an NCAA championship in 1993, but it was bittersweet in his family because the victory came against the Michigan Wolverines, the college team that both his father and grandfather had played with.

6. The Celtics once drafted a player named Ernesto Malcolm from Panama who went to Briar Cliff University.

7. The most players Boston has drafted from any school is 15. This mark was set by College of the Holy Cross, a private school in Massachusetts that produced Hall-of-Famers Tom Heinsohn and Bob Cousy.

8. Celtic forward Jayson Tatum went to Chaminade College Preparatory school, where he shared a physical education class with another student who would go on to become a high-level athlete: hockey player Matthew Tkachuk of the NHL's Calgary Flames.

9. Guard Dee Brown was lucky to be noticed by NBA scouts. Brown played at Jacksonville University, a school that does not traditionally receive much attention from NBA teams.

10. The Celtics have drafted seven players from Boston College, three from Boston University, and one from Boston State University. Not a single one of them has ever played for the team.

CHAPTER 5:

STATISTICALLY SPEAKING

QUIZ TIME!

1. What is Boston's franchise record for most victories club in a single regular season, which they set in 1972-73?

    a. 62
    b. 65
    c. 68
    d. 70

2. No one in Celtics history is within 750 assists of Bob Cousy at the top of Boston's record book.

    a. True
    b. False

3. Three players have recorded over 10,000 career rebounds for the Celtics. Which of the following has the most?

    a. Center Dave Cowens
    b. Center Bill Russell
    c. Center Robert Parish
    d. Forward Larry Bird

4. Who is the Celtics' single-season leader in steals, with 189?

   a. Guard David Wesley

   b. Forward Larry Bird

   c. Forward Paul Pierce

   d. Guard Rajon Rondo

5. Which Celtic really made his shots count, showing his accuracy with the highest career two-point field goal shooting percentage for the team, .628?

   a. Center Kendrick Perkins

   b. Forward Cedric Maxwell

   c. Center Daniel Theis

   d. Forward Gordon Hayward

6. The most personal fouls committed in any season by a Celtic player is 356. Which aggressive player established this club record?

   a. Center Dave Cowens

   b. Forward Tom Sanders

   c. Forward Sidney Wicks

   d. Guard Charlie Scott

7. Forward Paul Pierce attempted more than double the number of career free throws for the Celtics as guard Bob Cousy, who is in second place on the franchise list.

   a. True

   b. False

8. Which player holds the Boston record for most blocks in a single season, with 214?

a. Center Bill Russell

b. Center Robert Parish

c. Forward Kevin McHale

d. Center Tacko Fall

9. Which Celtic played more NBA games with the franchise than any other player?

a. Guard Sam Jones

b. Center Robert Parish

c. Forward Paul Pierce

d. Forward John Havlicek

10. The talented John Havlicek is Boston's all-time leader in points scored. How many points did he score for the team?

a. 26,395

b. 32,506

c. 38,117

d. 41,662

11. Larry Bird holds the single-season Celtic record for points per game. How many points did he average per game during that 1988 season?

a. 27.09

b. 27.66

c. 29.93

d. 31.54

12. Celtics legend John Havlicek *missed* more field goals during his career than any other Boston player has even *attempted*.

a. True

b. False

13. Which Celtic shooter sank the most free throws while playing with the club?

    a. Forward John Havlicek
    b. Guard Bob Cousy
    c. Forward Kevin McHale
    d. Forward Paul Pierce

14. On the Celtics' top 10 list for points scored by a player in a season, how many times does legend Larry Bird's name appear?

    a. 1
    b. 4
    c. 6
    d. 8

15. Three Boston Celtics have tallied more than 20,000 points for the team. Which of the following players did NOT reach that lofty threshold?

    a. Forward Paul Pierce
    b. Guard Bob Cousy
    c. Swingman John Havlicek
    d. Forward Larry Bird

16. Guard Isaiah Thomas hit 245 three-pointers during the 2016-17 season, which remains a franchise record.

    a. True
    b. False

17. Which Celtic recorded the highest career three-point shooting percentage with Boston, with .419?

    a. Guard Ray Allen
    b. Guard Marcus Thornton
    c. Guard Dana Barros
    d. Guard Eddie House

18. Which Celtic recorded the most rebounds in one season for the team, when he grabbed 1,930 loose balls?

    a. Center Robert Parish
    b. Forward Kevin Garnett
    c. Center Bill Russell
    d. Forward Kevin McHale

19. Which two teammates posted the highest combined steals total in a season for the Celtics, snatching 329 balls away from their opponents?

    a. Rick Fox and David Wesley in 1996-97
    b. Rajon Rondo and Kevin Garnett in 2009-10
    c. Larry Bird and Kevin McHale in 1980-81
    d. John Havlicek and Dave Cowens in 1970-71

20. Coach Tommy Heinsohn's 1972-73 season is the benchmark in terms of winning percentage, as he led the team to a .829 winning percentage in the regular season.

    a. True
    b. False

QUIZ ANSWERS

1. C – 68

2. A – True

3. B – Center Bill Russell

4. D – Guard Rajon Rondo

5. C – Center Daniel Theis

6. D – Guard Charlie Scott

7. B – False

8. B – Center Robert Parish

9. D – Forward John Havlicek

10. A – 26,395

11. C – 29.93

12. B – False

13. D – Forward Paul Pierce

14. B – 4

15. B – Guard Bob Cousy

16. A – True

17. B – Guard Marcus Thornton

18. C – Center Bill Russell

19. A – Rick Fox and David Wesley in 1996-97

20. A – True

DID YOU KNOW?

1. Three players have scored more than 20,000 points with the Celtics franchise. All three played forward for the team. John Havlicek set the record with 26,395, holding off Larry Bird and Paul Pierce to maintain the top spot on the list.

2. The Celtics hold the NBA record for the greatest improvement from one season to the next. In 2006-07, they finished with just 24 wins. But in the offseason, the team made blockbuster additions, importing forward Kevin Garnett and shooting guard Ray Allen, who boosted the team to 66 wins (and an NBA championship) in 2007-08.

3. The incomparable Bill Russell still stands as the player who has contributed to the most victories in team history. Russell accumulated 163.5 win shares during his career, almost 20 more than Larry Bird, who is second in Boston's history.

4. Larry Bird, perhaps the Celtics' most famous player, was known first and foremost as an excellent shooter. Not only was Bird the first player in NBA history to finish a season with shooting percentages above 50% on field goals, 40% on three-pointers, and 90% on free throws, he did it twice in a row. Steve Nash is the only other player to have achieved this feat multiple times in all the seasons since.

5. Celtics star Kevin Garnett was known for his intensity and versatility on the court. Garnett remains the only player in NBA history to finish his career with over 25,000 points, 10,000 rebounds, 5,000 assists, 1,500 steals, and 1,500 blocks.

6. Boston center Bill Russell was not only the first NBA player ever to secure over 20 rebounds per game in a season, but he did it in his first year in the league, 1957-58. Russell would go on to accomplish the feat 10 times during his career.

7. Center Bill Russel and forward John Havlicek hold the top spots in the Celtics record books when it comes to minutes per game. The indefatigable Russell averaged 42.3 minutes per game during his Celtics career, but Havlicek had the most impressive season, averaging 45.1 minutes a night in 1971-72.

8. Six players from the 1985-86 Boston Celtics championship team went on to become head coaches in the NBA. That list includes Larry Bird, Kevin McHale, Dennis Johnson, Rick Carlisle, Danny Ainge, and Sam Vincent.

9. The deadliest Celtic on the free-throw line was Ray Allen. He shot a team-record .914 from the stripe, making him the only player to finish with a Celtic career mark above .900.

10. In 1970-71, John Havlicek had the green light and fired 1,982 shots, which established the Celtics' record for most shots taken by one player in a single season. He scored 892

times. The following year, he actually took slightly fewer shots but scored 897 times, setting that record for Boston as well.

CHAPTER 6:

THE TRADE MARKET

QUIZ TIME!

1. With how many other NBA franchises have the Boston Celtics made a double-digit number of trades?

    a. 0

    b. 2

    c. 4

    d. 8

2. Boston has never in its history completed a trade with the Toronto Raptors.

    a. True

    b. False

3. In 2014, the Celtics traded coach Doc Rivers to the Los Angeles Clippers in an unusual swap. What did they receive in return?

    a. Guard Austin Rivers, Doc's son

    b. Clippers coach Vinny Del Negro

c. Swingman Chris Douglas-Roberts and guard Jabari Bird

d. A 1ˢᵗ round draft choice

4. The Boston Celtics twice traded popular forward Antoine Walker, once in 2003 and once in 2005. Which teams did they deal Walker to?

a. Atlanta Hawks and Minnesota Timberwolves

b. Memphis Grizzlies and Dallas Mavericks

c. Miami Heat and Minnesota Timberwolves

d. Dallas Mavericks and Miami Heat

5. Which useful Celtic player was NOT received from the San Diego Clippers in 1978 in exchange for Kermit Washington, Kevin Kunnert, Sidney Wicks, and Freeman Williams?

a. Guard Tiny Archibald

b. Center Robert Parish

c. Guard Danny Ainge

d. Forward Marvin Barnes

6. One of the Celtics' best trades saw them acquire star shooting guard Bill Sharman in exchange for center Chuck Share. Which team regretted making that deal with Boston?

a. St. Louis Hawks

b. Fort Wayne Pistons

c. Buffalo Braves

d. Los Angeles Lakers

7. Boston has completed more trades with the Indiana Pacers than with any other NBA franchise.

    a. True

    b. False

8. Which Celtic admitted that he was angry with his coach for telling him he would remain in Boston, saying: "Five days later, I found out I was being traded to Philadelphia. I can't tell you how much I felt betrayed. Either Pitino lied or something changed in a matter of a few days."?

    a. Guard Marcus Smart

    b. Forward Ricky Davis

    c. Center Brandon Bass

    d. Forward Dino Radja

9. Which of the following guards was NOT sent from the Celtics to the Cincinnati Royals/Sacramento Kings franchise in a trade?

    a. Danny Ainge

    b. Bob Cousy

    c. K.C. Jones

    d. Sam Cassell

10. Who did the Philadelphia 76ers select with the 1st overall draft pick acquired from the Boston Celtics in 2017?

    a. Point guard Ben Simmons

    b. Point guard Markelle Fultz

    c. Center Joel Embiid

    d. Center Jahlil Okafor

11. Which high-profile player who was sent in a trade from the Celtics to the St. Louis Hawks franchise went on to be elected to the Hall of Fame?

    a. Forward Dominique Wilkins
    b. Center Ed Macauley
    c. Forward Antoine Walker
    d. Guard Gary Payton

12. Boston has never completed a trade with the San Antonio Spurs.

    a. True
    b. False

13. In their history, the Boston Celtics and Orlando Magic have completed only one trade, involving three players. Which of the following players was NOT a part of the deal?

    a. Swingman Von Wafer
    b. Center Glen Davis
    c. Forward Geordie Harris
    d. Center Brandon Bass

14. Which player was involved in three separate trades that included a 1st-round draft pick during his career (including one to the Celtics and one from the Celtics)?

    a. Forward Antoine Walker
    b. Center Shaquille O'Neal
    c. Forward Wally Szczerbiak
    d. Center Raef LaFrentz

15. When the Celtics traded a 2nd-round draft choice to the Miami Heat in 1988, what did they receive from the Heat in return?

    a. A 1st-round draft choice in 1990

    b. Point guard Sherman Douglas

    c. Miami agreed not to select guard Dennis Johnson in the expansion draft.

    d. The use of a 60-foot yacht docked near the Miami Arena on which the team could party when visiting Florida

16. Forward Jae Crowder was traded from Boston to Cleveland in 2017 in what was a very difficult night for him. Not only was his life uprooted by the deal but Crowder's mother passed away just minutes after the trade was completed.

    a. True

    b. False

17. When the Celtics needed to rebuild and decided to trade stars Kevin Garnett, Paul Pierce, and Jason Terry away from Boston in 2013, which franchise did they send these players to in order to get the fantastic return of five players, four 1st-round draft choices, and a draft pick swap?

    a. Brooklyn Nets

    b. Minnesota Timberwolves

    c. Los Angeles Clippers

    d. Cleveland Cavaliers

18. Which players did Boston receive in return after sending 5th overall pick Jeff Green, Wally Szczerbiak, and Delonte West to the Seattle SuperSonics in 2007?

    a. Center Nenad Krstic and guard Nate Robinson
    b. Guard Rajon Rondo and forward Kevin Garnett
    c. Guard Ray Allen and center Glen Davis
    d. Forward Vin Baker and guard Shammond Williams

19. In 2000, the Celtics completed a large four-team trade, acquiring Robert Pack, Hot Rod Williams, a draft choice, and cash. The team sent out Dana Barros and Danny Fortson. Which of the following other teams was NOT involved in this complicated deal?

    a. New York Knicks
    b. Dallas Mavericks
    c. Golden State Warriors
    d. Utah Jazz

20. Boston general manager Jan Volk once proposed a deal to the Chicago Bulls that would have sent Celtics icon Larry Bird to the Windy City in exchange for a young Michael Jordan.

    a. True
    b. False

QUIZ ANSWERS

1. C – 4

2. B – False

3. D – A 1st-round draft choice

4. D – Dallas Mavericks and Miami Heat

5. B – Center Robert Parish

6. B – Fort Wayne Pistons

7. B – False

8. D – Forward Dino Radja

9. C – K.C. Jones

10. B – Point guard Markelle Fultz

11. B – Center Ed Macauley

12. A – True

13. C – Forward Geordie Harris

14. D – Center Raef LaFrentz

15. C – Miami agreed not to select guard Dennis Johnson in the expansion draft.

16. A – True

17. A – Brooklyn Nets

18. C – Guard Ray Allen and center Glen Davis

19. A – New York Knicks

20. B – False

DID YOU KNOW?

1. Boston has only acquired an actual player from the Charlotte Hornets once. They have made two trades with Charlotte, acquiring several draft picks, but point guard Kemba Walker was the only player obtained from this franchise.

2. The Celtics and Los Angeles Lakers have had a fairly heated rivalry throughout their existence, particularly during the 1980s. The two teams have set aside their dislike for each other to make a trade only three times in Boston's long tenure in the NBA. The Celtics were on the better end of each of those trades.

3. Dealing a Hall-of-Famer can be difficult, but the Celtics made it work exceptionally well in 1956. Their star, Ed Macauley, wanted to be sent to St. Louis where he had family, including a son who was ill. Boston agreed and traded him to the St. Louis Hawks in exchange for a draft pick, which they used on another eventual Hall-of-Famer, center Bill Russell.

4. Boston and Phoenix have a rich history of trades throughout the years. The Celtics have made more trades with the Suns than with any other franchise. Significant names moved between the two teams include Paul Silas, Paul Westphal, Dennis Johnson, Joe Johnson, Tony Delk, Rajon Rondo, and Isaiah Thomas.

5. In 1980, Boston made a franchise-changing deal with the Golden State Warriors, trading away the 1st overall selection in the NBA draft along with another 1st-round draft choice. In return, the Celtics received center Robert Parish and another draft pick that they used on forward Kevin McHale. Together, the duo won three NBA championships.

6. In a 2003 draft-day trade, the Celtics acquired high school center Kendrick Perkins, who had been selected by the Memphis Grizzlies. Although they did not draft him directly, this was the first time in franchise history that they'd acquired an American player who had not attended college.

7. One of the worst trades made by the Celtics occurred in 1979 when they sent center Tom Barker and three 1st-round draft picks to the New York Knicks for center Bob McAdoo. McAdoo lasted just 20 games with Boston, providing one win share for the team, while New York's haul ended up giving the Knicks 71.5 win shares over time.

8. In 2005, the Celtics were part of a five-team deal along with the New Orleans Hornets, Utah Jazz, Miami Heat, and Memphis Grizzlies. The deal involved 13 players, with the Celtics shipping out Antoine Walker and receiving Albert Miralles, Qyntel Woods, Curtis Borchardt, and two 2nd-round draft picks. Although none of the players Boston

received found much success in the league, this trade remains the largest swap in NBA history to this day.

9. In a deal that was very unpopular at the time, Boston dealt playoff hero Isaiah Thomas (who had led the Celtics to crucial playoff victories right after learning that his sister had been killed in a car accident) to the Cleveland Cavaliers. Thomas, Jae Crowder, Ante Žižić, and draft picks were sent to Cleveland for the ostensible upgrade of point guard Kyrie Irving. Irving remained with the Celtics for just two seasons before signing with the Brooklyn Nets.

10. One of the largest and most impactful trades ever made by the Celtics was completed on July 31, 2007, with the Minnesota Timberwolves. Boston sent Sebastien Telfair, Ryan Gomes, Theo Ratliff, Gerald Green, Al Jefferson, two 1st-round picks, and cash to Minnesota for power forward Kevin Garnett. Even without considering the money, the seven assets given up by the Celtics is an NBA record in any trade for a lone player.

CHAPTER 7:

DRAFT DAY

QUIZ TIME!

1. Which prospect did the Celtics select with their first-ever draft choice in 1947?

    a. Center George Hauptfuhrer from Harvard
    b. Swingman Gene Stump from DePaul
    c. Center Chuck Share from Bowling Green
    d. Swingman Bulbs Ehlers from Purdue

2. The Celtics have never held the 1st overall pick in the NBA draft.

    a. True
    b. False

3. How high did Boston select power forward Kevin McHale in the 1980 NBA Entry draft?

    a. 1st round, 3rd overall
    b. 2nd round, 43rd overall
    c. 4th round, 75th overall
    d. 7th round, 222nd overall

4. Which point guard did the Celtics select highest in the NBA Entry draft, using a 3rd overall pick to add the floor general to their team?

    a. North Carolina Central's Sam Jones in 1957

    b. Colorado's Chauncey Billups in 1997

    c. Jacksonville's Dee Brown in 1990

    d. Oklahoma State's Marcus Smart in 2014

5. Who was the first player ever selected by the Celtics in the NBA Entry draft to be their lone selection for a single year?

    a. Forward Rick Fox in 1991

    b. Center Darius Songaila in 2002

    c. Guard Dee Brown in 1990

    d. Guard Danny Ainge in 1981

6. Which player, drafted by the Celtics, went on to score the most NBA points for another team after leaving Boston?

    a. Swingman Joe Johnson

    b. Guard Chauncey Billups

    c. Center Al Jefferson

    d. Forward Antoine Walker

7. Boston has drafted precisely one player who has played a single game in the NBA. Forward Roger Strickland hit the court for just four minutes during that one game but he did make a basket, finishing his NBA career with 2 points.

    a. True

    b. False

8. The Celtics have looked overseas for talent frequently in the NBA Entry draft and have selected two players from one specific nation, more than they have chosen from any other country besides America. Which nation was it?

   a. Australia

   b. Brazil

   c. Croatia

   d. Russia

9. It is not hyperbole to say that the Boston Celtics' 1956 draft was one of the best in all professional sports. The Celtics selected three future Hall-of-Famers, including all of the following except which one?

   a. Center Bill Russell

   b. Guard K.C. Jones

   c. Forward Tom Heinsohn

   d. Guard Bob Cousy

10. Who was the first player ever drafted by the Celtics who came directly from high school, rather than suiting up for a traditional college team?

   a. Forward Tony Battie

   b. Center Al Jefferson

   c. Guard Kemba Walker

   d. Forward Jayson Tatum

11. When the NBA merged with the ABA in 1976 and two teams (the Kentucky Colonels and the Spirits of St. Louis) were disbanded, who did the Celtics select in the resulting dispersal draft?

a. Center Randy Denton from the Spirits of St. Louis

b. Forward Ron Boone from the Spirits of St. Louis

c. Guard Bird Averitt from the Kentucky Colonels

d. No one; they passed on their selection.

12. Twice during the 2000s, Boston has traded away all of its draft picks or selected players on draft day.

a. True

b. False

13. The Celtics struck out mightily in the 1979 NBA draft, selecting nine players who scored a total of how many points in the NBA?

a. 0

b. 30

c. 264

d. 412

14. Of the draft spots in the top 10 in the NBA draft, which spot has Boston selected at more than any other?

a. 3rd overall

b. 6th overall

c. 8th overall

d. 10th overall

15. Superstar forward Larry Bird was drafted by Boston with the 6th overall pick in the 1978 NBA Entry draft. Which player did the Portland Trail Blazers select 1st overall ahead of him?

a. Phil Ford of the North Carolina Tar Heels

b. Rick Robey of the Kentucky Wildcats

c. Mychal Thompson of the Minnesota Golden Gophers

d. Ron Brewer of the Arkansas Razorbacks

16. Guard Danny Ainge was such a talented athlete coming out of college that he was drafted in three sports (basketball, baseball, and football).

   a. True

   b. False

17. Up to and including the 2020 NBA Entry draft, how many player selections have the Boston Celtics made in their history?

   a. 188

   b. 236

   c. 470

   d. 609

18. How many times in history has Boston used a top 10 overall draft pick (not including times they have immediately traded such a pick)?

   a. 17

   b. 24

   c. 28

   d. 36

19. With which selection in the NBA draft did the Celtics draft future Hall of Fame inductee JoJo White in 1969?

   a. 7th overall

   b. 9th overall

   c. 43rd overall

   d. 112th overall

20. There have been 26 players in the NBA who measured 7'3" or taller. The Celtics have never drafted any of them.

    a. True

    b. False

QUIZ ANSWERS

1. D – Swingman Bulbs Ehlers from Purdue

2. B – False

3. A – 1st round, 3rd overall

4. B – Colorado's Chauncey Billups in 1997

5. C – Guard Dee Brown in 1990

6. A – Swingman Joe Johnson

7. A – True

8. C – Croatia

9. D – Guard Bob Cousy

10. B – Center Al Jefferson

11. D – No one; they passed on their selection.

12. A – True

13. B – 30

14. A – 3rd overall

15. C – Mychal Thompson of the Minnesota Golden Gophers

16. B – False

17. C – 470

18. D – 36

19. B – 9th overall

20. B – False

DID YOU KNOW?

1. On June 17, 1986, the Boston Celtics made All-American college star Len Bias their top choice in the NBA draft, selecting him with the 2nd overall pick. The small forward was dead two days later, tragically passing away from cardiac arrhythmia brought on by an overdose of cocaine.

2. Despite the major draft success of guard Chauncey Billups, who went on to play more than 1,000 NBA games, score more than 15,000 points, and hand out more than 5,000 assists, the Celtics have never selected another player from the University of Colorado.

3. Of all the players drafted by Boston, small forward Paul Pierce leads in most games played (1,343) and most points scored (26,397) with the team, edging out forward John Havlicek by just 2 points.

4. In the 2016 and 2017 NBA drafts, Boston held the 3rd overall choice. In both years, the Celtics chose a small forward with their premium picks; Jaylen Brown from California in 2016 and Jayson Tatum from Duke in 2017.

5. The Celtics' first draft pick who went on to play 1,000 NBA games was forward John Havlicek, whom the team drafted 7th overall from Ohio State University in 1962. Havlicek became a franchise icon, eventually seeing his number retired and being elected to the Hall of Fame.

6. Boston has held the 16th overall pick 10 times, more than any other spot in the draft. Twice, they elected to trade the selection. When keeping it, their best draft pick from the spot was guard Terry Rozier, taken from the University of Louisville in 2015.

7. The largest Celtics draft class ever was selected in 1973, when the team drafted 19 players (one per round). Only their top two choices, Steve Downing of Indiana University and Phil Hankinson of the University of Pennsylvania, ever played with the team, but neither lasted even one full season.

8. The Boston Celtics hold the distinction of breaking the color barrier in basketball by drafting the first black athlete ever taken by an NBA club. In the 1950 draft, owner Walter A. Brown selected swingman Chuck Cooper with the 14th overall pick in the 2nd round, famously stating: "I don't give a damn if he's striped, plaid, or polka-dot, Boston takes Charles Cooper of Duquesne." Cooper played four years with the Celtics.

9. Forward Jeff Green was drafted high by the Celtics (with the 5th overall pick in 2007). But, due to a draft-day trade to the Seattle SuperSonics, it was over three years before Green actually stepped on the court in a Boston uniform after being traded back to the squad in 2011.

10. The latest pick the Celtics have made in the NBA draft was Dan Trant from Clark University, whom the team chose 228th overall in the 10th round in 1984. Trant never made it

to the NBA. Mark Minor, the team's 165th overall pick from Ohio State University in the 11th round in 1972, was the latest pick they've made who actually played for the team. Minor lasted just four games in the NBA.

CHAPTER 8:

THE GUARDS

QUIZ TIME!

1. Which guard played more minutes than any other for Boston during the team's challenging first season in the NBA in 1946-47, suiting up for 55 games and finishing 3rd on the team in scoring?

   a. Jerry Kelly
   b. Wyndol Gray
   c. Charlie Hoefer
   d. Art Spector

2. Boston's defensive stalwart Dennis Johnson loved "D" beyond just great defense on the court; he married a wife named Donna and had children named Dwayne, Daniel, and Denise.

   a. True
   b. False

3. Which swingman has recorded the most career turnovers while with the Boston Celtics?

a. Rajon Rondo

b. Antoine Walker

c. Paul Pierce

d. Danny Ainge

4. Which guard has played the most minutes for the Celtics?

a. Paul Pierce

b. Bob Cousy

c. Sam Jones

d. John Havlicek

5. The initials in popular Celtics point guard K.C. Jones's name stand for what?

a. Nothing; they are his proper given name.

b. Kevin Curtis

c. Karl Christopher

d. Kenneth Chadwick

6. Shooting guard Sam Jones played his entire NBA career with the Boston Celtics after coach Red Auerbach drafted him in the 2nd round in 1957 despite never having seen Jones play before. How long did Jones's career last?

a. 8 seasons

b. 10 seasons

c. 12 seasons

d. 15 seasons

7. It is a Celtic tradition for every point guard to lob an alley-oop for each teammate during the warm-up before a home playoff game.

a. True

b. False

8. Which of the following is NOT true about quirky Celtics point guard Kyrie Irving?

   a. He has stated on multiple occasions in public forums that he believes the earth is flat.

   b. His godfather is former NBA point guard Rod Strickland.

   c. He is very musical; Irving is a strong singer and dancer in addition to playing the baritone saxophone.

   d. He has reserved a seat on a space shuttle from a company that sells future civilian trips to the moon.

9. Which Celtics point guard holds the franchise record for most assists in a single game, with 24?

   a. Kyrie Irving in 2018

   b. Bob Cousy in 1962

   c. Rajon Rondo in 2010

   d. Sherman Douglas in 1994

10. Point guard Rajon Rondo leads all Boston guards in career triple-doubles. Rondo recorded his first such game for the Celtics against which NBA team on December 3, 2008?

   a. Indiana Pacers

   b. Orlando Magic

   c. New York Knicks

   d. Los Angeles Clippers

11. Celtics mainstay Bob Cousy played over 900 NBA games with the club. Where does he rank in games played all-time for Boston?

    a. 1st overall

    b. Tied for 3rd overall

    c. 4th overall

    d. 6th overall

12. Years after his playing and coaching careers were both over, Boston shooting guard Sam Jones became a substitute teacher in Maryland.

    a. True

    b. False

13. Which of the following positions has popular Celtics shooting guard Danny Ainge NOT held with Boston after retiring from his playing career?

    a. Head coach

    b. Executive director of basketball operations

    c. General manager

    d. Team president

14. Which of these current Celtic guards has been with the team for six seasons, the longest current tenure in Boston's backcourt?

    a. Shooting guard Jaylen Brown

    b. Point guard Marcus Smart

    c. Shooting guard Romeo Langford

    d. Point guard Jeff Teague

15. Which of the following statements about Celtics shooting guard John Havlicek is NOT true?

    a. He attended the Cleveland Browns training camp after being drafted by the team.
    b. He was an early investor in the world-famous Wendy's fast-food restaurant chain.
    c. He is third all-time in most NBA championships won and had an 8-0 record in NBA Finals.
    d. He owned a horse named Celtic Pride that once finished second in the Kentucky Derby.

16. Former Celtic point guard Bob Cousy was the first guard in NBA history to be ejected from a game, after he committed consecutive flagrant fouls on opposing forward Wilt Chamberlain, just 28 seconds apart.

    a. True
    b. False

17. One Celtic guard set an NBA record by leading the league in assists for eight consecutive seasons. Which player did it?

    a. Rajon Rondo
    b. Danny Ainge
    c. Bob Cousy
    d. K.C. Jones

18. Boston point guard Kyrie Irving played in the 2016 Summer Olympics in Rio de Janeiro for the United States of America despite being born in which country?

a. Canada

b. United Kingdom

c. Australia

d. Brazil

19. Which hard-nosed Boston guard once taunted opposing 7'1" center Tree Rollins so mercilessly that the two fought and Rollins chomped down on the Celtic's finger, necessitating two stitches and prompting the headline "Tree Bites Man"?

a. Paul Pierce

b. Rajon Rondo

c. Ray Allen

d. Danny Ainge

20. Celtic guard Dennis Johnson set an interesting record by recording 39 consecutive assists to the same player (teammate Larry Bird).

a. True

b. False

QUIZ ANSWERS

1. B – Wyndol Gray

2. A – True

3. C – Paul Pierce

4. D – John Havlicek

5. A – Nothing; they are his proper given name.

6. C – 12 seasons

7. B – False

8. D – He has reserved a seat on a space shuttle from a company that sells future civilian trips to the moon.

9. C – Rajon Rondo in 2010

10. A – Indiana Pacers

11. D – 6th overall

12. A – True

13. A – Head coach

14. B – Point guard Marcus Smart

15. D – He owned a horse named Celtic Pride that once finished second in the Kentucky Derby.

16. B – False

17. C – Bob Cousy

18. C – Australia

19. D – Danny Ainge

20. B – False

DID YOU KNOW?

1. It would be hard for anyone to surpass the legacy of Celtic legend Bob Cousy on the court. But Cousy himself may have left an even greater legacy off the court, as he convinced fellow players to form the National Basketball Association Players Union in 1954 to improve conditions for all future athletes. Cousy was the union's first president and this contributed to his selection for the Presidential Medal of Freedom by President Donald Trump in 2019.

2. Only one athlete in history has been honored as a first-team high school All-American in basketball, football, AND baseball. That was former Celtic guard and current Boston general manager and president of basketball operations, Danny Ainge.

3. Popular Celtic guard Isaiah Thomas got his name from Hall of Fame Detroit Pistons guard Isiah Thomas. The father of Boston's Thomas was a Los Angeles Lakers fan who bet the naming rights of his unborn son against a friend who was a Pistons fan. When Detroit beat L.A. for the 1989 NBA title, the friend chose the baby's name (and may have set his future career path in motion).

4. Well-respected Celtics shooting guard Ray Allen was known for his intense drive and preparation, which led to a beautiful and efficient shooting form. Allen is the Celtics'

record-holder for best free throw percentage in a season, shooting .952 in 2008-09 and sinking 72 free throws in a row during that same season, which is also a record for Boston players.

5. In an unprecedented twist of fate, the Celtics had more to deal with than the terrible emotional fallout after shooting guard Reggie Lewis died of a sudden cardiac trauma in 1993. There was no method for the NBA to revoke his contract, so Lewis's agreement counted against Boston's salary cap for two further seasons afterward. Other NBA teams voted against granting an exemption.

6. After his retirement, Boston shooting guard Bill Sharman remembered the anxiety and buildup of energy he had felt on game days. As a coach, Sharman created a morning shootaround as a way for his players to alleviate nerves and keep themselves occupied. The practice is now commonly used by every NBA team.

7. Six point guards who have played for the Celtics have been enshrined in the Basketball Hall of Fame. The most recent was Jo Jo White, who was elected in 2015.

8. Nate "Tiny" Archibald achieved great individual success in the NBA before coming to Boston, as he once led the league in scoring and assists in the same season. But the great player's only title came when he joined the Celtics and won a championship with the team in 1981.

9. The first three-pointer in NBA history was made in Larry Bird's first game with the Boston Celtics on October 12,

1979, against the Houston Rockets. The shot was not made by Bird, however, but by Celtic guard and future coach Chris Ford.

10. Many NBA players consider themselves tough. Celtic guard Jo Jo White could back that up, as he served for two years with the United States Marines before playing basketball with Boston. He credited this time for his exemplary conditioning.

CHAPTER 9:

CENTERS OF ATTENTION

QUIZ TIME!

1. Where was champion Celtic center Bill Russell born?

    a. Brooklyn, New York

    b. Detroit, Michigan

    c. Monroe, Louisiana

    d. Tampa Bay, Florida

2. Celtic center Robert Parish, who played 14 years with the team, was born and raised in Boston, Massachusetts.

    a. True

    b. False

3. Only one center has played an entire career of at least 10 years for the Celtics without ever starting a game for another NBA franchise. Which loyal center played only for Boston?

    a. Al Jefferson

    b. Dave Cowens

    c. Bill Russell

    d. Robert Parish

4. Which of the following is NOT true regarding the intelligence of current Boston center Tacko Fall?

    a. He learned to speak English in just eight months.

    b. He held a 4.0 grade point average during his high school career.

    c. He scored in the 95th percentile when he took the SAT before entering college.

    d. He earned his degree in computer science in just two years by taking summer courses.

5. A Boston center holds the NBA record as the player elected to the Naismith Memorial Basketball Hall of Fame at the youngest age. Which Celtic was selected for inclusion at only 32 years old?

    a. Bill Walton

    b. Bill Russell

    c. Ed Macauley

    d. Dave Cowens

6. Boston Celtics legendary center Bill Russell won 11 championships during his career, which is the most ever in the NBA and ties him for first place all-time in North American sports history with which other athlete?

    a. Henri Richard of the National Hockey League's Montreal Canadiens

    b. Babe Ruth of Major League Baseball's New York Yankees

    c. Tom Brady of the National Football League's New England Patriots

d. Wayne Gretzky of the National Hockey League's Edmonton Oilers

7. After his playing career, Celtic center Dave Cowens ran as a Republican candidate for Massachusetts Secretary of the Commonwealth but he was defeated.

    a. True
    b. False

8. What was the term given to the strategy that opposing teams used to slow down Celtic center Shaquille O'Neal, who was a notoriously bad free-throw shooter?

    a. The O'Neal Oh No
    b. The Shaq Psyche
    c. The Hack-a-Shaq
    d. The Brick Layer

9. Which of the following training techniques, unique during his playing days, did Boston center Robert Parish NOT use to develop the remarkable longevity of his 21-year NBA career?

    a. Yoga
    b. Vegetarianism
    c. Cryotherapy
    d. Martial arts

10. Outgoing Celtic center Shaquille O'Neal also released six rap albums in his spare time. Which of these albums became a platinum-selling hit record?

    a. *Shaq Fu: Da Return*
    b. *Shaq Diesel*

c. *Shoot Pass Slam!*

d. *You Can't Stop The Reign*

11. Celtics big man Bill Russell is one of only four players ever to accomplish which of the following feats on the court?

    a. Leading two different countries to gold medal victories at the Summer Olympics

    b. Playing an entire career with only one franchise while winning an NBA championship

    c. Recording over 30 rebounds in a single NBA game

    d. Winning the NCAA championship and NBA championship in consecutive years

12. Boston pivot Robert Parish led the NBA in field goal percentage in just his second season in the league.

    a. True

    b. False

13. Two Boston centers share the unusual fate of having won the NBA's MVP award without having been named to the All-NBA First Team during the same season. Which two Celtics were simultaneously recognized for their achievements and ignored?

    a. Bill Russell and Dave Cowens

    b. Al Horford and Robert Parish

    c. Bill Russell and Kevin Garnett

    d. Ed Macauley and Arnie Risen

14. John Kundla, the head coach of the Los Angeles Lakers, showed massive respect for one particular Celtic, center

Bill Russell, when he uttered which of the following quotes to the media in 1959?

    a. "I thought their team was average at four of the five positions, but there's just no way to get around that center."

    b. "Give us Bill Russell and we'd sweep even an All-Star team! We'd be the best basketball team of all time."

    c. "We don't fear the Celtics without Russell. Take him out and we can beat them. He's the guy who whipped us psychologically."

    d. "They might as well put a lid on the basket when Russell is back there. He guards that hoop like it's Fort Knox."

15. Which of the following facts about current Senegalese Celtic center Tacko Fall is NOT true?

    a. He holds the NBA record for largest wingspan with a stretch of 8'2.25."

    b. He has held small roles as a warrior in the television shows *Game of Thrones* and *Vikings*.

    c. He trained in the United States of America, learning moves and skills from another center born in Africa, the legendary Hakeem Olajuwon.

    d. His first NBA points with the Celtics came on a slam dunk which he did not even jump to complete.

16. No Celtic center has ever led the team in points scored during a single game.

    a. True

    b. False

17. Celtics pivot Bill Russell retired in 1969, but still holds the NBA record for most rebounds in one half of a basketball game. How many loose balls did he pull down against Philadelphia in that half on November 16, 1957?

    a. 19

    b. 23

    c. 28

    d. 32

18. Longtime Boston center Robert Parish holds the NBA record for most regular-season games played in his career, with 1,611. How many of those contests came while Parish was with the Celtics?

    a. 948

    b. 1,106

    c. 1,493

    d. 1,611

19. Which of the following is NOT true about former Boston center Bill Walton?

    a. He appeared in the hit 1984 movie *Ghostbusters*, starring Bill Murray.

    b. He owns vacation homes in four different states and six other countries.

    c. He records his own radio show for satellite radio, "One More Saturday Night."

    d. He suffered so much pain from his basketball injuries that at one point he considered suicide.

20. President Barack Obama awarded Boston center Bill Russell the Presidential Medal of Freedom in 2011 for his incredible career and contributions to the civil rights movement.

   a. True
   b. False

QUIZ ANSWERS

1. C – Monroe, Louisiana

2. B – False

3. C – Bill Russell

4. D – He earned his degree in computer science in just two years by taking summer courses.

5. C – Ed Macauley

6. A – Henri Richard of the National Hockey League's Montreal Canadiens

7. A – True

8. C – The Hack-a-Shaq

9. C – Cryotherapy

10. B – *Shaq Diesel*

11. D – Winning the NCAA championship and NBA championship in consecutive years

12. B – False

13. A – Bill Russell and Dave Cowens

14. C – "We don't fear the Celtics without Russell. Take him out and we can beat them. He's the guy who whipped us psychologically."

15. B – He has held small roles as warriors in the television shows *Game of Thrones* and *Vikings*.

16. B – False

17. D – 32

18. B – 1,106

19. B – He owns vacation homes in four different states and six other countries.

20. A – True

DID YOU KNOW?

1. Although he remains in the discussion about the greatest basketball player of all time, Celtic center Bill Russell struggled in his youth to pick up the fundamentals of the sport and was actually cut from his junior high team in Oakland.

2. Center Dave Cowens had an excellent career in Boston but he paid for it physically. Cowens suffered over 30 ankle sprains, two broken legs, and a fractured foot while in the NBA but always played with great intensity and brought the same fire to his numerous rehabs.

3. During his rookie season in the NBA, future Celtic center Shaquille O'Neal twice dunked the ball so powerfully that it destroyed the backboard, causing the NBA to strengthen the design of the nets after the season.

4. Boston big man Bill Russell famously vomited before most games early in his career. As he became more used to the NBA, teammates noted that he would only throw up before a significant game or major challenge, such as facing rival center Wilt Chamberlain.

5. The Celtics' Tacko Fall stands 7'5" tall, making him the tallest player currently in the NBA. Not only that, but he is also among the top 50 tallest living human beings in the entire world. However, Fall is two inches short of the NBA

height record, set by Sudanese center Manute Bol and tied by Romanian center Gheorghe Muresan.

6. Center Zaid Abdul-Aziz holds an interesting place in the Boston record books, though not for his statistical accomplishments. Of over 450 players who have suited up for the Celtics over the years, Abdul-Aziz is listed 2nd alphabetically by his last name (behind forward Alaa Abdelnaby), and 2nd last alphabetically by his first name (ahead of only center Zan Tabak).

7. Future Celtic center Bill Russell's style of play was so innovative defensively that the NCAA re-wrote two rules because of it. In his third year, they increased the width of the paint to keep him further away from the basket defensively. Later, after Russell left college for the NBA, the NCAA also outlawed basket interference.

8. Talented center Pervis Ellison never really got much chance to show his skill in Boston. After suffering several injuries (including a broken toe that occurred as he tried to move some furniture), Ellison played in just 69 games during his tenure with the Celtics. They played 246 games while he was with the team.

9. Even though the team finished with a losing record in 1977-78, Celtics star big man Dave Cowens had a season to remember personally. That year, Cowens paced the team in points, rebounds, assists, blocks, and steals, marking the first time in NBA history a player had accomplished that feat.

10. Center Al Horford was a celebrated addition to the Boston Celtics when he signed as a free agent in 2016. Horford's longest tenure was not with Boston, though, but with the Dominican Republic's national basketball team. Born there in 1986, Horford has played for the country since 2008.

CHAPTER 10:

THE FORWARDS

QUIZ TIME!

1. What did master trash talker and two-time defending champion of the NBA's Three-Point Shootout contest Larry Bird famously say when he entered the All-Star locker room in 1988 before competing in (and winning) the event for a third consecutive time?

   a. "Don't even bother…you guys might as well sit this one out."
   b. "Anybody up for a little wager?"
   c. "Nope…I don't see any competition in here."
   d. "So, who's coming in second tonight?"

2. Respected Boston forward Paul Silas played for five different NBA teams and later became the head coach of five different NBA teams, without ever taking a head coaching position in a city where he had played.

   a. True
   b. False

3. Which Boston forward defected from his home country to play for the Celtics but was legally ordered to leave America and return to his place of birth?

   a. Nenad Krstic
   b. Wally Szczerbiak
   c. Dino Radja
   d. Kelly Olynyk

4. Hall of Fame player Charles Barkley said which opposing Boston forward "...was the best player I played against because he was unstoppable offensively, and he gave me nightmares on defense."?

   a. Larry Bird
   b. Cedric Maxwell
   c. Kevin Garnett
   d. Kevin McHale

5. Celtic forward M.L. Carr went on to become president of which WNBA franchise after his playing and coaching careers came to an end?

   a. Cleveland Rockers
   b. Charlotte Sting
   c. Las Vegas Aces
   d. Dallas Wings

6. What did physical Celtic forward Xavier McDaniel do throughout his career to intimidate opposing players?

   a. Walk to center court before tip-off and flex his considerable biceps toward whomever he was guarding that night

b. Wear a set of brass knuckles on each hand to the games, noticeably taking them off just before the start

c. Growl like a pit bull whenever he went up for a rebound

d. Shave his head completely, including his eyebrows

7. Small forward Paul Pierce, who starred for the Celtics for 15 years, hated the team as a child because he grew up in California as a fan of the Los Angeles Lakers.

   a. True
   b. False

8. Boston forward Sidney Wicks spent parts of three seasons with the Celtics but had absolutely terrible timing. Which of the following results did NOT occur in Wicks' career?

   a. The Celtics won the NBA title in 1975-76, the year before Wicks arrived in Boston.
   b. The Trail Blazers won the NBA title in 1976-77, the year after Wicks left Portland.
   c. The Celtics won the NBA title in 1979-80, the year after Wicks left Boston.
   d. The Celtics won another NBA title in 1980-81, two years after Wicks left Boston.

9. Which of the following is NOT true about Celtics franchise superstar Larry Bird's legacy with the general public?

   a. Seventeen years after his retirement, Bird was still appearing in McDonald's commercials with contemporary basketball stars like LeBron James and Dwight Howard.

b. The ubiquitous media company, Twitter, chose "Larry" as the name of its logo, to honor Larry Bird.

c. Larry David, of *Seinfeld* and *Curb Your Enthusiasm* fame, named his son Larry "not after myself, but after the best shooter of all time, Larry Bird."

d. A man who was convicted of a robbery in Oklahoma City requested that his sentence be increased from 30 years to 33 years because Bird wore jersey No. 33.

10. Celtic forward Don Nelson became a legendary Hall of Fame coach in his retirement and, after retiring from coaching, he started a farm in Hawaii where he grows each of the following products except for which one?

   a. Coffee
   b. Flowers
   c. Cannabis
   d. Pineapples

11. Evan Turner recovered from a difficult start to his life to become a small forward for the Boston Celtics. Which of the following is NOT a disease Turner contracted before he had even reached one year old?

   a. Pneumonia
   b. Measles
   c. Mumps
   d. Asthma

12. Despite earning over $108 million during his NBA playing days, Celtics power forward Antoine Walker filed for bankruptcy just two years after leaving the league.

a. True

b. False

13. Which of the following is NOT an activity accomplished by Celtics power forward Thomas "Satch" Sanders after he retired from the NBA?

   a. Becoming head coach of the Boston Celtics

   b. Completing the Boston Marathon in a time of three hours and seventeen minutes, just over an hour off of world record pace

   c. Founding the Rookie Transition Program to help new players acclimatize to life in the NBA after leaving college

   d. Becoming the first African-American head coach in any sport for an Ivy League college, as the basketball coach at Harvard

14. Longtime Celtic forward Rick Fox holds dual nationality from which two countries?

   a. America and France

   b. Great Britain and New Zealand

   c. Israel and America

   d. Canada and Bahamas

15. The diversity of star forward Paul Pierce's game can be shown through his Celtics records. Which of the following is NOT a Boston team record held by Pierce?

   a. Most three-point field goals made in a career (1,578)

   b. Most steals in a single game (9)

c. Most free throws made without missing in a single playoff game (21)

   d. Most rebounds accumulated in an overtime period (14)

16. Celtics legend Larry Bird and Lakers icon Magic Johnson wrote a book together about their friendship and rivalry called *When the Game Was Ours*.

   a. True

   b. False

17. With which unorthodox form did Celtic forward Don Nelson prefer to shoot his free throws?

   a. Under-handed, with the ball starting between his legs

   b. One-handed and under-handed, using a scoop style similar to bowling

   c. One-handed, pushing the ball with only his right hand

   d. Over-handed, using two hands in a soccer throw-in style

18. Which of the following stars has Celtics legend Larry Bird NOT appeared in a movie with?

   a. Nick Nolte, in *Blue Chips*

   b. Dan Aykroyd, in *Celtic Pride*

   c. Bill Murray, in *Space Jam*

   d. Tom Cruise, in *Jerry Maguire*

19. What do popular Celtics swingman (and later coach) M.L. Carr's initials stand for?

a. Martin Luther
b. Matthew Lawrence
c. Michael Leon
d. Maxwell Lucius

20. Celtic forward Rick Fox has a second career as a professional actor. Fox has appeared in over 50 motion pictures and television shows between 1994 and 2020.

a. True
b. False

QUIZ ANSWERS

1. D – "So, who's coming in second tonight?"

2. A – True

3. C – Dino Radja

4. D – Kevin McHale

5. B – Charlotte Sting

6. D – Shave his head completely, including his eyebrows

7. A – True

8. C – The Celtics won the NBA title in 1979-80, the year after Wicks left Boston

9. C – Larry David, of *Seinfeld* and *Curb Your Enthusiasm* fame, named his son Larry "not after myself, but after the best shooter of all time, Larry Bird."

10. D – Pineapples

11. C – Mumps

12. A – True

13. B – Completing the Boston Marathon in a time of three hours and seventeen minutes, just over an hour off of world record pace

14. D – Canada and Bahamas

15. D – Most rebounds accumulated in an overtime period (14)

16. A – True

17. C – One-handed, pushing the ball with only his right hand

18. D – Tom Cruise, in *Jerry Maguire*

19. C – Michael Leon

20. A – True

DID YOU KNOW?

1. During the early years of the NBA, salaries were not high enough for players to live on year-round. During the offseason in the 1950s, power forward Tommy Heinsohn was an insurance salesman. Small forward Gene Guarilia made money playing guitar. Even coach Red Auerbach was part owner of a Chinese restaurant.

2. In addition to being talented, Celtic forward Cedric Maxwell was popular, confident, and outgoing. Maxwell played to the fans by openly mocking rival Los Angeles Lakers stars. He once wore a pair of Kurt Rambis's signature glasses to poke fun at Rambis and he also pointed out James Worthy's poor free-throw shooting by mimicking a choking gesture between Worthy's shots from the line.

3. The biggest rivalry in the NBA during the 1980s was Celtics versus Lakers and specifically Boston forward Larry Bird versus Los Angeles guard Magic Johnson. It's debatable which star got the better of the matchup, though Celtics fans point to MVP trophies (three for Bird, two for Johnson) as a sign that Bird was the victor.

4. Before hitting the big time as an NBA star, Celtic forward Don Nelson had some humble beginnings. As a youth growing up on a farm, Nelson had to shoo chickens out of the way so he could practice his shooting in the yard by

firing shots through a bike wheel with the spokes removed that was nailed to his shed.

5. Boston icon Tom Heinsohn had a dream career as a forward for the Celtics. Heinsohn played for nine seasons in the NBA, and went to the NBA Finals in all nine of those seasons, winning eight titles along the way.

6. Before Canadian forward Kelly Olynyk made it to the NBA as a big man with the Boston Celtics, another member of his family beat him to the big leagues. Olynyk's mother, Arlene, was the NBA's first female scorekeeper. She served in that position with the Toronto Raptors from 1995 to 2004.

7. Longtime Celtics star forward Paul Pierce owes a lot to his teammate, center Tony Battie... including his life. After Pierce was stabbed 11 times at a Boston nightclub in 2000, Battie reacted quickly to get Pierce to the nearest hospital, where the doctors saved him. Pierce made a full recovery.

8. After the 1986 death of newly drafted Celtic forward Len Bias due to a cocaine overdose, President Ronald Reagan signed into effect the "Len Bias Law," which increased the mandatory minimum sentences for drug crimes throughout the country.

9. Current Boston forward Jaylen Brown is also known for his academic pursuits off the court. Brown plays chess, studies history and philosophy, and is learning Spanish. He has given talks at elite Boston-area institutions such as MIT and Harvard and was the youngest player ever elected as vice president of the NBA Players Association.

10. Boston coach Red Auerbach is credited with making small forward Frank Ramsey into the first "Sixth Man" used in NBA history. Despite possessing starting caliber skills, Ramsey was more at ease entering the game later. Auerbach theorized that not only would Ramsey feel better but he would also have more energy when others were tired and the move was soon copied by many other teams.

CHAPTER 11:

COACHES, GMS, & OWNERS

QUIZ TIME!

1. Who served as the Celtics' first general manager?

    a. David C. Gavitt

    b. Walter A. Brown

    c. Red Auerbach

    d. Danny Ainge

2. Boston coach Jim O'Brien married the daughter of Hall of Fame NBA coach Jack Ramsay.

    a. True

    b. False

3. The Celtics' first head coach, John Russell, lasted for how long in that position with the franchise?

    a. 12 games

    b. 1 season

    c. 2 seasons

    d. 9 seasons

4. The Celtics' most recent coach, Brad Stevens, rose through the coaching ranks to lead which NCAA program?

    a. Georgia Tech Yellow Jackets
    b. West Virginia Mountaineers
    c. Purdue Boilermakers
    d. Butler Bulldogs

5. Who has owned the Boston Celtics for the longest amount of time?

    a. Paul Dupee, Don Gaston, and Alan N. Cohen
    b. Boston Basketball Partners L.L.C.
    c. Ira Levin and Harold Lipton
    d. The Boston Garden-Arena Corporation

6. Of all those who have coached the Celtics for over 100 NBA games, which one had the lowest winning percentage at only .293?

    a. M.L. Carr
    b. John Russell
    c. Rick Pitino
    d. Jim O'Brien

7. Boston is the only NBA franchise to have a player rise from playing for the team to ownership of the team.

    a. True
    b. False

8. Which coach led the Celtics to their first NBA championship?

    a. Alvin Julian
    b. Bill Fitch

    c. Tom Heinsohn

    d. Red Auerbach

9. Which Boston general manager once took the floor as a player on the team before getting the chance to guide it from the front office?

    a. Chris Wallace

    b. Danny Ainge

    c. Larry Bird

    d. K.C. Jones

10. Who is the Boston leader in all-time coaching wins with the franchise?

    a. Doc Rivers

    b. Tom Heinsohn

    c. Brad Stevens

    d. Red Auerbach

11. When iconic Celtic coach and general manager Red Auerbach felt that the team had secured a victory, how did he frequently and memorably celebrate?

    a. By falling asleep in his chair

    b. By pulling his starters and sending in a roster of backup players

    c. By lighting up and smoking a cigar in the arena

    d. By turning his back on the game and calling his wife

12. Celtic coach Doc Rivers never quit, nor was he fired by the team, but he left in an unusual manner when the Los Angeles Clippers offered Boston a 1st-round draft pick to let Rivers come coach for them instead.

a. True

b. False

13. How many of the Celtics' 17 head coaches have spent their entire NBA coaching career with Boston?

    a. 0

    b. 3

    c. 5

    d. 11

14. Which Celtic general manager has led the franchise to the most playoff appearances?

    a. Jan Volk

    b. Red Auerbach

    c. Danny Ainge

    d. Walter A. Brown

15. Out of 16 seasons coaching the Celtics, how many times did coach Red Auerbach finish above .500 and qualify for the NBA playoffs in the same season?

    a. 10

    b. 12

    c. 13

    d. 16

16. At one point in their history, the Celtics employed four coaches over a dozen years who had all started for Boston as players.

    a. True

    b. False

17. How did Paul Gaston become the majority owner of the Boston Celtics in 1993?

    a. He purchased the team when the previous owners wished to sell.
    b. He was given the team by his father as a gift.
    c. He forced a takeover of the corporation that had previously owned the team.
    d. He was hired as CEO of the company that owned the team.

18. Current Celtic coach Brad Stevens had a job at which restaurant chain when he began his coaching career as an unpaid volunteer?

    a. Outback Steakhouse
    b. Red Lobster
    c. T.G.I. Fridays
    d. Applebee's

19. Which Celtic coach is the only one of the following NOT to have won the NBA Coach of the Year Award while behind the bench for Boston?

    a. Brad Stevens
    b. Tom Heinsohn
    c. Bill Fitch
    d. Red Auerbach

20. Celtics owner Harry T. Mangurian Jr. once proposed trading franchises with New York Yankees owner George Steinbrenner, as part of a business deal.

a. True
b. False

QUIZ ANSWERS

1. B – Walter A. Brown

2. A – True

3. C – 2 seasons

4. D – Butler Bulldogs

5. B – Boston Basketball Partners L.L.C.

6. A – M.L. Carr

7. B – False

8. D – Red Auerbach

9. B – Danny Ainge

10. D – Red Auerbach

11. C – By lighting up and smoking a cigar in the arena

12. A – True

13. C – 5

14. B – Red Auerbach

15. D – 16

16. A – True

17. B – He was given the team by his father as a gift.

18. D – Applebee's

19. A – Brad Stevens

20. B – False

DID YOU KNOW?

1. Among others, the Boston Celtics have been owned at different times by a husband and wife (Walter A. Brown and later Marjorie Brown), a father and son (Don Gaston and later Paul Gaston), and two breweries (Knickerbocker Brewing Company and Ballantine Brewery).

2. Only one man has served as both coach and general manager of the Celtics. Arnold "Red" Auerbach handled the personnel duties for 33 years and coached the team for 16 years during that tenure before giving up his bench boss duties to appoint another Boston legend, Bill Russell, as player/coach.

3. Boston's first-ever assistant coach, Danny Silva, was more of a baseball man. Silva played professional baseball, including one major league game with the Washington Senators, and later became commissioner of the Cape Cod Baseball League.

4. Some coaches are just better at the college level. Legendary floor general Rick Pitino won NCAA championships both before and after guiding the Celtics but never managed a playoff berth or even a winning record during his four years in Boston.

5. The Celtics became pioneers in 1966 when team legend Bill Russell, still playing with the club, was hired in a dual role as head coach. Russell became the first African-American

in any major North American sport to earn a head coaching position.

6. Boston has employed seven team presidents during its illustrious history. Founder Walter A. Brown held the title for the franchise's first 17 years but Red Auerbach nearly doubled that mark, serving in the position for 31 years.

7. The Celtics have never had a head coach who was born outside the United States. They have also never had a coach who was born in Boston. They have employed four head coaches from New York, which was the home state of Red Auerbach, Honey Russell, Satch Sanders, and Rick Pitino.

8. John "Honey" Russell, the first-ever coach of the Boston Celtics, enjoyed a lengthy professional basketball career for 25 years and played for over 40 different teams during that span. Not one of those teams was a Boston squad.

9. Only two African-Americans have won more than a single NBA championship as the head coach of a team. Both accomplished it with the Boston Celtics. Bill Russell did it in 1968 and 1969, and K.C. Jones matched the feat in 1984 and 1986.

10. Twice in league history, Boston general managers have been awarded the NBA Executive of the Year Award. Red Auerbach received the honor in 1979-80, and Danny Ainge took home the award in 2007-08.

CHAPTER 12:

THE AWARDS SECTION

QUIZ TIME!

1. Which Celtic has won the most Maurice Podoloff Trophies as league MVP while playing for Boston?

   a. Forward Larry Bird

   b. Guard Bob Cousy

   c. Center Bill Russell

   d. Forward John Havlicek

2. The first Celtic to win any major NBA award was franchise center Bill Russell, who took home his first MVP award in 1958.

   a. True

   b. False

3. During which season did the Celtics win their first Larry O'Brien Trophy as NBA champions?

   a. 1949-50

   b. 1952-53

   c. 1954-55

   d. 1956-57

4. In 1996, the NBA announced its 50 Greatest Players in NBA history. How many of these players suited up for the Celtics?

   a. 6
   b. 9
   c. 14
   d. 21

5. The J. Walter Kennedy Trophy, given to an NBA player who shows "great service and dedication to the community," has been awarded to which Celtic?

   a. Guard Danny Ainge
   b. Forward Paul Pierce
   c. Center Kelly Olynyk
   d. No Celtic has ever won this award.

6. How many Celtics have won the Twyman-Stokes Trophy as NBA Teammate of the Year thanks to "selfless play and commitment and dedication to his team"?

   a. 0
   b. 2
   c. 6
   d. 11

7. In the team's illustrious history, no Boston Celtic has ever led the NBA in scoring for a single season.

   a. True
   b. False

8. Who was the most recent Boston player to make the NBA All-Rookie First Team?

   a. Forward Jaylen Brown
   b. Forward Jayson Tatum
   c. Center Tacko Fall
   d. Guard Rajon Rondo

9. Eight times in NBA history, a Celtic player has taken home the NBA All-Star Game MVP Award. Who was the most recent player to do so?

   a. Forward Kevin Garnett in 2009
   b. Guard Nate Archibald in 1981
   c. Guard Bob Cousy in 1957
   d. Forward Larry Bird in 1982

10. How many All-Star Game selections have been earned by players suiting up for the Boston Celtics in the year in which they were selected?

    a. 92
    b. 118
    c. 146
    d. 204

11. The Sixth Man of the Year Award, for best performing player as a substitute, has been won by which two Celtics in franchise history?

    a. Swingman Frank Ramsey and forward Kevin McHale
    b. Forward Kevin McHale and center Bill Walton
    c. Center Bill Walton and forward John Havlicek
    d. Forward John Havlicek and guard Gerald Green

12. Guard Dee Brown is the only Boston Celtic ever to be crowned the NBA's Slam Dunk Contest champion, taking home the title over forward Shawn Kemp of the Seattle SuperSonics.

    a. True
    b. False

13. Which of the following Celtic players did NOT win the Eddie Gottlieb Trophy as the league's top rookie?

    a. Forward John Havlicek
    b. Forward Tom Heinsohn
    c. Forward Larry Bird
    d. Center Dave Cowens

14. Of the Celtics in the Basketball Hall of Fame, big man Ed Macauley was the first to play with Boston. What year did he begin playing with the team?

    a. 1950
    b. 1953
    c. 1957
    d. 1960

15. Which of the following Celtic players has been selected to the fewest NBA All-Star Games while playing for Boston?

    a. Forward Kevin Garnett
    b. Guard Bob Cousy
    c. Forward Kevin McHale
    d. Center Robert Parish

16. Guard Isaiah Thomas won the NBA's Community Assist Award for "community engagement, philanthropic activity, and charity work" in 2016-17 and was matched by Boston forward Jaylen Brown in 2019-20.

   a. True
   b. False

17. Standout Celtics shooter Larry Bird won the first three NBA Three-Point Contests. Who is the only other NBA player to win the contest three times?

   a. Boston Celtic forward Paul Pierce
   b. Golden State Warriors guard Steph Curry
   c. Chicago Bulls guard Craig Hodges
   d. Sacramento Kings forward Peja Stojakovic

18. Who was the Boston player who most recently made the NBA All-Defensive First Team?

   a. Forward Kevin Garnett in 2011-12
   b. Guard Marcus Smart in 2019-20
   c. Guard Dennis Johnson in 1986-87
   d. Guard Avery Bradley in 2015-16

19. In which year(s) did Boston host the NBA's annual All-Star Game?

   a. 1962
   b. 1951, 1983
   c. 1955, 1974, 1988
   d. 1951, 1952, 1957, 1964

20. For almost two decades, computer company IBM gave an award to the NBA player judged by its programming formulas to be most valuable to his team. Forward Paul Pierce received the award for Boston.

    a. True
    b. False

QUIZ ANSWERS

1. C – Center Bill Russell

2. B – False

3. D – 1956-57

4. C – 14

5. D – No Celtic has ever won this award.

6. A – 0

7. A – True

8. B – Forward Jayson Tatum

9. D – Forward Larry Bird in 1982

10. C – 146

11. B – Forward Kevin McHale and center Bill Walton

12. B – False

13. A – Forward John Havlicek

14. A – 1950

15. A – Forward Kevin Garnett

16. A – True

17. C – Chicago Bulls guard Craig Hodges

18. B – Guard Marcus Smart in 2019-20

19. D – 1951, 1952, 1957, 1964

20. B – False

DID YOU KNOW?

1. The Joe Dumars Trophy, for sportsmanship, ethical behavior, fair play, and integrity, has never been won by a Boston Celtic. Interestingly, it has never been won by a member of the team's biggest rival, the Los Angeles Lakers, either.

2. Each year, the NBA denotes three teams' worth of All-NBA players, and the Celtics have been well represented. Guard Bob Cousy landed on the first team 10 times, the most of any player, while forward Larry Bird made it nine times. Including selections to the second and third teams, Cousy is still the leader with 12 selections, ahead of forward John Havlicek and center Bill Russell, who had 11 apiece.

3. Only four players have earned the NBA's relatively new Lifetime Achievement Award. Despite this exclusivity, two of them were Boston Celtics. Center Bill Russell was the first recipient in 2016-17, and forward Larry Bird was honored with the award in 2018-19.

4. When the NBA announced its top 10 teams in history in 1996, two Boston teams were included on the list. The 1964-65 edition of the Celtics made the cut, landing the first spot on the chronological list. The 1985-86 version of the team was also selected and was noteworthy as the 5th highest winning percentage ever recorded.

5. Former NBA MVP center Bill Walton was traded to the Boston Celtics near the end of his career and spent two years with the team, winning both an NBA championship and the NBA's Sixth Man of the Year Award while coming off the bench for the squad.

6. Only five NBA players have ever won both the MVP and Defensive Player of the Year Awards. Celtic forward Kevin Garnett is one of those five and is the only Celtic in the franchise's long history to have won Defensive Player of the Year.

7. Celtic forward Bailey Howell was born in Tennessee but made a major impression while playing collegiate basketball at Mississippi State University. To this day, the state of Mississippi awards the Howell Trophy to the best male college basketball player of the year.

8. The NBA has named its Finals MVP trophy after a Boston Celtic: legendary center Bill Russell. Commissioner David Stern bestowed the new trophy name in 2009, and Russell himself handed it to Los Angeles Lakers guard Kobe Bryant when Bryant became the winner that year.

9. The great Larry Bird is the only person in history to have won the NBA's MVP, Coach of the Year, and Executive of the Year awards. He took home three MVP awards while playing for the Celtics, then eventually returned to his home state of Indiana where he won the other awards with the Pacers franchise.

10. Two Celtics have been elected to the Naismith Memorial Hall of Fame twice, both as a player and as a coach. Guard Bill Sharman and forward Tommy Heinsohn both earned this achievement, though Sharman coached with four other franchises, but never Boston.

CONCLUSION

There you have it, an amazing collection of Celtics trivia, information, and statistics at your fingertips! Regardless of how you fared on the quizzes, we hope that you found this book entertaining, enlightening, and educational.

Ideally, you knew many of these details but also learned a good deal more about the history of the Boston Celtics, their players, coaches, management, and some of the quirky stories surrounding the team. If you got a little peek into the colorful details that make being a fan so much more enjoyable, then mission accomplished!

The good news is the trivia doesn't have to stop there! Spread the word. Challenge your fellow Celtics fans to see if they can do any better. Share some of the stories with the next generation to help them become Boston supporters too.

If you are a big enough Celtics fan, consider creating your own quiz with some of the details you know that weren't presented here, and then test your friends to see if they can match your knowledge.

The Boston Celtics are a storied franchise. They have a long history with multiple periods of success (and a few that were less than successful). They've had glorious superstars, iconic moments, hilarious tales...but, most of all, they have wonderful, passionate fans. Thank you for being one of them.

Made in the USA
Las Vegas, NV
25 November 2022

60211598R00075